Second Skin

✧

Stories & Poems

Terry Hertzler

Caernarvon Press
San Diego

FIRST EDITION

Library of Congress Cataloging-in-Publication Data

Hertzler, Terry.
    Second skin : stories & poems / Terry Hertzler.-- 1st ed.
        p. cm.
    ISBN 0-9716383-2-2 (pbk. : alk. paper)
    I. Title.
    PS3608.E644S43 2003
    811'.54--dc21

                                        2003010560

Printed on acid-free paper

Caernarvon Press
4435 Marlborough Avenue #3
San Diego, CA 92116

Table of Contents

Life

A Dialogue with My Favorite Author
March 1959

The door to the phone booth squeaked
as I closed it carefully,
shutting out sounds of traffic
from the street beyond.
Wiping my sweaty hands on my jeans,
I unfolded a yellow slip of paper
and stared at the name scribbled there:
James Kjelgaard. Author of *Big Red*, *Haunt Fox*,
Stormy and *Fire-Hunter*—the finest books
a nine-year-old boy could imagine.

I stood, dime gripped tightly in my hand,
remembering the sudden surge of excitement when
yesterday, having finished his latest masterpiece,
I'd read on the inside back cover, "James Kjelgaard
and his wife make their home in Phoenix, Arizona."
Phoenix, Arizona! That's where I live.
James Kjelgaard lives in my town!

And so, trembling inside,
I now stood in the phone booth,
afraid to attempt so vital a call from home,
the dime hot in my palm, almost slipping
as I dropped it in the slot.
I held my breath as I dialed.
It rang—once, twice.
    "Hello?"
    "Is this James Kjelgaard?"
    "Yes it is."
    "Is this the James Kjelgaard who writes books?"
    "Yes it is."
    "Thank you," I said
and hung up.

America Online — 1995

so i'm into this 15-minute conversation about poetry
with someone whose online screen name is *phloppy1*,
arguing the value of workshops and rewriting, and i'm
beginning to lose patience with this person, who thinks poetry
should be written only by inspiration and never revised,
when we finally get around to the age/sex question
and i find out i've been talking to a 14-year-old girl
and it blows both our minds for several seconds
and i'm looking at my cursor just sitting there on the screen
not moving, and i'm thinking, "wow" (i think in lowercase
online, since uppercase is shouting and impolite), when she
types back, "really? you're 45? that's how old my parents
are!" weird," and i think, yeah, weird, but i'm no longer
so upset with her naive suppositions about writing
and we talk for several more minutes before her mother
yells at her to turn off the computer and go to bed
and i think of the implications for communication
that only cyberspace offers, where each of us
is safely tucked in our own little corner and can be reached
only to the extent we desire, and what really amazes me
is that this young woman and i were able to engage
in a conversation online that would probably never take place
in the real world—a conversation between (i imagine)
a skinny teenager with braces and acne who shops
at stores in the mall i've never even entered and listens
to music by groups with names like *puppie vomit*,
and a middle-aged man who sometimes pulls
a favorite book down from his shelf and holds it
for a few moments, unopened, just because he likes
the smell and feel and idea of books, a conversation
where, for a short time, the two are peers exchanging ideas
independent of race, sex, age or other distinguishing
characteristics, a conversation where only the words matter,
thoughts marching nakedly across the screen—and i realize
that even though the poetry (and conversation) online
is the same mixture you find elsewhere—mostly mediocre
to bad, with an occasional jewel, "fragile as the lifeline
of a snowflake"—that even though there are tremendous
limitations to conversing keyboard-to-keyboard

and it's unfortunate we live in a world that presents
so many barriers to understanding and communication,
that this impersonal beige box of silicon chips and glowing
phosphor dots offers opportunities we can experience no
other way (i talked to a poet in india the other night!).
i hope *phloppy1* keeps writing; she'll get better with time
and practice. i know i will. even my typing is improving.

Fat
September 1989

I haven't had a hamburger in two weeks—I've given up
red meat for my health. The fat man in my mirror
should be pleased.

It's Friday night. I ate fish. If I were Catholic
and it were twenty years ago, the pope would be pleased.

When I was 20, I'd see fat men and think
I'm never going to let that happen to me. How ugly.
How sad. Don't they care?

The fat man in my mirror laughs. Twenty years ago
I weighed 135 pounds. I was in Vietnam
living off Ritz crackers and Coca Cola
and sleeping with an M-16.

Twenty years ago. My eating habits haven't changed much.
But I'm breathing hard on 40 now, and I sit at a desk
all day long. That's better than the Nam, but not good exercise.

I no longer jog, and my ten-speed sits in the bedroom.
Once a month I dust it off and pump up the tires.
I don't ride it, just dust it off and pump up the tires.
The fat man in my mirror is tidy. Anal retentive,
an old girlfriend once said.

I'm married now. Took me thirty-six years to make that leap.

Twenty years ago I was skinny and scared most of the time
and lonely more often than scared. I'm not lonely anymore.
Maybe that's why I've given up red meat. The fat man
in my mirror shrugs. I think I'll go have a carrot stick.

At the Fair

". . . It slices, it dices, it trims nose hair, cuts your grass, weaves strands of recovered lint into comforters so warm you'll never buy a wool blanket again, cleans ugly grease stains from any fabric but is safe enough to drink and supplies more vitamin C than a gallon of orange juice, inflates flat tires in seconds, washes, waxes and repaints your car in one easy step, is potent enough to grow hair on an egg but prevents diaper rash under even the most strenuous of conditions, freshens your breath, cleans silver, brass, stainless steel, mirrors, windows, false teeth, is an ideal toy for children of all ages, repairs broken china, glues almost anything to anything and is the perfect tool for performing minor surgeries in your own home, kills mites, spiders and bugs of all sorts, shines shoes, clears up severe acne overnight, makes the perfect glaze for holiday turkeys or hams, allows you to reach those hard-to-clean places with its patented flex-O-stenxion three-piece fiber-optic Magic Wand, increases your IQ by 20 percent, improves your sex life, predicts the future and creates résumés that will guarantee you the perfect job, turns common dirt into gold, grants up to three wishes, and is available here today for only three easy payments of $19.95. Buy two and save even more!"

Ideas

"I admire you writers," the student said, "your imagination—
where do you get your ideas?"

And I want to tell her the ether is full of ideas,
that anyone who has lived more than 10 or 15 years
and is paying attention has material enough for a lifetime,
that ideas are easy—it's execution that causes pain,
the endless, aching struggle to transform those incandescent
bursts of wordless joy or horror into words on a page
that turns writers bitter, turns normal human beings
into isolated, bleary-eyed oddities whose sense of fashion
or propriety or capacity to deal with the exigencies of life
is so distorted that mothers comfort other mothers
with sympathetic hugs while secretly sighing, *thank god
my child is not a writer*—that writers are cursed with ideas
that churn and bubble and pop to the surface in blinding
flashes of fire and light that scream WRITE ME! or whisper
a never-ending litany of oh me, oh me, oh me, oh please
you must write me, until they swirl like rivers, bursting
the frail, inadequate levees writers throw up to stem
the flow—I want to tell this child I write not for fame
or love or admiration—I write to keep my chin
above the flood.

To Write a Poem

Look at the world. See how it spins by.
Grab one of the world's legs
with both hands and hold tight.
Your grasp will begin to slip.
Open your mouth wide
and bite the world's leg. Sink
your teeth into its flesh, feel
the world's blood fill your mouth, run
down your chin. Your eyes
will sting and you will begin
to choke—but hold on a little
longer—you will hear a high
whistling sound that is either the wind
or crows laughing or bells from a cathedral
you visited when you were eight.
Wait until you almost recognize
music in the wind or the laughter
or the bells, then let go.
                              You will find yourself
sitting in a lush meadow or perhaps by the sea
with a wide path of green tiles leading
down into the water, disappearing
under the waves. Or perhaps you will be
wading through a swamp. It doesn't matter.
You will want to spit. Do so.
In your hand you will find a broken tooth.
Your tongue will tell you it is
one of your own. Look at the tooth.
Its enamel will be spider-webbed
with a pattern that is both complex and compelling.
Follow the pattern with your eyes. You will
become dizzy. Lie down. If you
are in a meadow, the grass will be soft;
if you are by the sea, the green tiles
will be warm from the sun; if you are in
a swamp, you will be miserable and cold, but
embrace the snakes, float on your back
with your ears below the surface
of the water and listen in your bones

to the thrumming of the frogs. Sleep.
When you awake, a single word
will rest on your tongue.
Swallow it whole. It
may be bitter, but more will follow.

At the Poetry Festival

". . . how could I not
Be only myself, this dream of flesh, from moment to moment."
— Mark Strand

After the former Poet Laureate
and Pulitzer Prize winner read
his beautiful words—this many honored

teacher of the Committee on Social
Thought—he shook back his silver locks,
bowed to the applause, accepted the arm

of his lovely companion, and moved
to the rear of the auditorium—where
as the next poet began her performance

he began to beguile his young blonde friend
with what I'm sure were words of wonder.
To those of us near him, though, his words

boomed, set after set of moronic waves
beating their thoughtless way toward shore.
A man turned in his seat to glare, but the poet

ignored him, his years of facing occasionally
indifferent audiences proof against so slight
a criticism. A woman sighed and moved

to the other side of the auditorium. On stage
the poet continued her reading. Behind me
the poet continued his monologue, rising

to greet admirers who approached to touch
the hem of his trousers and plead, "Tell us again
how you made the sun stand still or turned

water into wine." And the great man smiled,
licked his golden lips with his golden tongue
and droned on.

The Football Game

I spent the first half sitting on the bench
next to David Arthur, watching nervously
as play moved up and down the field,
avoiding the coach as he thumped back and forth
along the sideline yelling encouragement
and instructions to the boys on the field.
We were losing to Light & Life Christian Academy, 21-14.

We were the Bible Chapel Christian Grade School
6th grade flag football team. David Arthur and I were
last-minute substitutes, recruited because the flu
had sidelined several regular players and we were
all that was left in the limited pool of male 6th graders
at Bible Chapel. We were the smallest boys in the 6th grade.

Neither of us had played organized football before.
"It's for the school, boys," the coach had said, "for the team."
David and I had both looked doubtful, but acquiesced.

In the first play of the second half, Greg Bonaventure,
our right guard, was accidentally knocked to the ground
and twisted his leg (I say accidentally since in flag football,
like basketball, knocking opponents to the ground
is prohibited).

As Greg limped off the field, coach Brower turned
to look at David and me. "David," he called, waving
toward the field. David promptly turned a pale shade
of chartreuse and threw up.

"Okay, Terry," said coach Brower, his equanimity unruffled,
"you go in for Greg." My heart beat fast; blood rushed
past my ears so loud I wasn't sure I'd heard the coach right.
"Me?" I asked.

"Get in there—hurry up," said coach Brower, raising his arm
and pointing toward the field like Moses parting the Red Sea.
I hurried onto the field. As if in the eye of a hurricane I moved
in a cone of subdued light and sound. All around me,
yet far away, was noise and movement. The coach's arms
and legs jerked wildly, his mouth opening and closing

without sound; the cheerleaders, miles away,
shook worm-like pompoms in slow motion.

I took my place on the line and looked up.
Like a bubble bursting, sound and color
flooded back, time leaped sideways
and the player facing me across the line growled.

This huge, hulking monster with no neck
and forearms the size of my legs grinned at me
and growled. And the ball was snapped and
I was looking at the sky, amazed at how blue it was
and how luminous the clouds were and how nice it was
just to lie on my back in the grass contemplating
the roundness of the world, until a face loomed
into view and I saw it was the coach's face and I realized
my chest hurt and he was helping me to my feet
and I noticed my finger was bleeding, and
I didn't know why, and the coach sat me on the bench,
patted me on the head and said, "You'll be all right."

We lost the game. The only play in which I participated—
the one and only organized football game in which
I ever played—resulted in our quarterback fumbling
the ball, which was picked up by Light & Life's defense
and run back for a touchdown.

The final score was 35-17. After my one play,
Greg Bonaventure was sent back in, his leg apparently
recovered sufficiently to permit his return. David Arthur
never entered the game. . . .

I eventually became quite good at table tennis
and rollerskating, but I never developed much interest
in team sports. Over the years, however, I've spent
much time lying on my back in the grass, amazed
at how blue the sky is and how luminous the clouds
can sometimes be, contemplating the roundness
of the world.

Doors

My office has no windows, no door. It barely has walls.
Around me I hear the frail plastic sound of fingertips
on keyboards, like mice chewing the air. The phone
in the cubicle next to mine rings all day. Along the corridor,
computers whisper "you have mail" and the air conditioner
roars like a distant battle. On my monitor, the cursor blinks
at me, steady as a Guernsey cow, as if asking "What now,
what now?" and I feel the fluorescent tubes above me
flicker an elaborate code while dark, twisted things-for-which-
I-lack-a-name swim in hazy circles in my eyes. I hear voices
down the hallway, low and metallic, a sudden soft sneeze
from nearby.

And for some unknowable reason, I'm seized
by a vivid memory of a bedroom, some stranger's
home—I must have been four or five—a door closing
as my brother and I were admonished, "Shhh, it's nap time.
Close your eyes. Rest."

I have no idea who the person was or where we were
but the ceiling was slanted, as if an attic, and the sunlight
through sheer white curtains illuminated millions
of dust particles that rose and fell and swirled like children
playing tag in a schoolyard. The room was warm
and the bedspread, beaded with tiny balls like a field
of friendly ants, was soft and cool on my cheek.
I remember especially the door, old and solid,
with an elaborate grain that seemed to flow down its length
like a slow river, shiny and deep, as if hundreds of hands
had stroked and rubbed it until it gleamed with dark fire,
almost dancing in my sleepy eyes.

And it must have been autumn then, for I remember
afterwards, after our nap, outside, the leaves were bright
and crisp and piled at our feet like a gift.

Climbing

He'd always been a climber. At six, he climbed
the antenna attached to a neighbor's house.
A frantic search by his mother, face like chalk,
eyes rimmed with red, found him happily sitting
on the roof grinning at the clouds.

And trees, as high as he could climb, branches
so tentative he knew another foot would plunge him
to earth.

At 19, a paratrooper (the only thing he liked
about the Army), the C-119 shuddering as it climbed,
props beating a rhythm that seemed to shout *jump,
jump*—a step into emptiness, earth and sky tumbling
as the long fall began.

And in Arizona at 25, backpacking the Mogollon Rim,
a natural tank filled with spring runoff, his friends diving
into clear, deep water as he climbed the cliff face rising
along its southern edge. Three-quarters of the way
to the top handholds disappeared, and looking back
he realized up was easy, down problematic. He clung
to the side, weighing options, wondering how deep
the water really was—and for a moment watched clouds
crossing the sky like vast, unconquerable fortresses,
then let go.

Toast

Warm Saturday morning in June,
late breakfast of orange juice
and whole-wheat toast,
lazing in my recliner,
Car Talk on the radio,
thinking about running the vacuum
or maybe dusting—when
I swallow wrong, chunk of toast
down the wrong pipe, choking,
bright flashes of light,
then darkness . . .

. . . and I regain consciousness
sprawled on the floor, throat
aching, thoughts jumbled, a small
lump of toast on the carpet
inches from my head, heavy chair
overturned by my fierce struggles
for air—and I sit up,
stunned by the realization
I could have died just now.

And I notice my shirt is soaked.
I change clothes, pull on sneakers,
walk to Balboa Park, where
for the rest of the afternoon
I sit watching the trees and birds,
a small boy on a bicycle
with training wheels proudly riding
next to his mother, a bush whose
name I'm ignorant of covered with
tiny blue flowers, and at least three
different kinds of clouds—cirrus,
cumulus, maybe altocumulus—and
the sun is warm and all day long
I keep swallowing.
It's all so delicious.

My Grandmother and Me — A Fragment

The photograph is old, black & white, small:
two-and-a-half by three-and-a-half inches.
I found it stuck in the pages of *Early Autumn*,
a novel that won Louis Bromfield a Pulitzer Prize
in 1926. Bromfield was born in my hometown,
Mansfield, Ohio, nine days short of 53 years
before me. (I wonder, was he as disappointed
as I at being born so close to Christmas?) My mother
had attended school with one of his daughters
and once was invited to a party at their farm,
the same farm at which Humphrey Bogart
and Lauren Bacall were later married. It was,
my mother said, the fanciest place she had ever seen;
they had a separate room the size of a large closet
just for the telephone. With red velvet drapes.
Red velvet drapes, a table, chair, and the French
telephone. That's all.

I am five or six at the time of the photograph
(it could have been taken the year Bromfield died).
It's winter. I know this because, though it was taken
indoors, I'm wearing a heavy, dark winter coat,
fleece-lined, with one of those large collars
that could be pulled up to protect the back
of your head and ears and cheeks, ideal for the long
bitter Ohio winters. I think, too, it must have been
just after Christmas. Strapped around my waist
over my coat is a pair of cap guns with pearl handles
and fancy black holsters. I remember them clearly.

It was the Christmas we lived in the big brick house
on South Main, the one with so many rooms
and a servant's entrance and the long wooden banister.
I loved that house even though strangers lived there
with us. I had wanted to wear my new guns to bed
that Christmas night, and I remember my mother saying
cowboys didn't wear their guns to bed as she placed
my pistols carefully in the hall linen closet outside my
room, where I'd know they'd be safe till morning.

We must have driven down to Portsmouth that winter, making a weekend of it, for the roads then made the trip an all-day affair, especially in December or January. We would have stayed with my dad's brother in his small white house, and his wife would have made peanut brittle, and my brother and I would have slept on cots in the living room. And sometime during that weekend we'd have taken a morning or an afternoon to visit the place that was something like a hospital to see my dad's mother. That's when the photograph must have been taken.

There are only two of us in the photograph, my grandmother and me. She sits in a wooden chair. I stand next to her. The top of my head almost reaches her cheekbones. The chair might be a rocker, but I can't be sure since the photograph ends at my knees. The top third is blank wall. The chair is solid-looking, with arms that curve and are higher in the front than in back. My grandmother leans against a pillow that is crocheted with a diagonal pattern of small dark squares. Each square consists of 16 dots. My grandmother is wearing a short-sleeved floral print dress and there are two large white buttons on a vertical line above her waist. I can't tell if there are more buttons because her arms are crossed in front of her. The top of the dress is held closed at the neck with either a small hook or a pin.

I'm not sure who took the photograph, but it was an adult, probably my mother, standing in front of me with the camera angled to the left to include my grandmother. The photograph was taken with a flash. I can tell this because of the shadows. You can tell a lot from shadows—sometimes what you can't see in a photograph is more important than what you can see.

I'm fascinated with this photograph, perhaps because I know so little about my grandmother, perhaps because of the faces. Although our arms almost touch, there's no connection, no interaction between us. I can almost hear my parents saying, "Go stand next to your grandma so we can get a picture."

Later, when I was a teenager, I would lie under trees
on late autumn afternoons when dark bare branches
seemed pasted to the sky and take snapshots
with my Instamatic. I thought this would make dramatic,
artistic photographs.

And when I was thirty, a fire destroyed every print
and negative I had stored at my office. I had been working
as a photographer for almost seven years at the time,
but it wasn't my professional work I missed most.

In 1969, at nineteen, I was sent to Vietnam.
I spent thirteen months there and I like to believe
I used the 35mm camera I'd purchased through the PX
more than I used my rifle. I still have the camera.
Most of the photographs, however, were lost in the fire.
And in some of those prints were faces like my
grandmother's. There's something about the angle
of the head, the line of the mouth and, especially
the eyes—eyes that seem to stare directly into yours
while looking away—eyes that are all pupil, black
and shining and lost.

Nanosecond

I was at my sister's playing Trivial Pursuit with her
and my brother-in-law, Paul, a long-haul trucker,
when he drew the question, "What's a nanosecond?"
Without hesitation he answered, "How long
our lovemaking lasts."

My sister turned red, and Paul & I looked at each other
and started laughing. And couldn't stop. After a minute,
my sister stood up and left the room, which was too bad
since I was winning the game.

Time, as Einstein so eloquently demonstrated, is relative,
moves at rates that defy the precision of gears, the oscillation
of quartz crystals. As a boy I had a rock collection, my favorite
a beautifully polished chunk of rose quartz. Quartz
is piezoelectric, generates an electrical charge
in response to mechanical pressure, vibrates
when voltage is applied. That amazes me.
Clocks in rocks.

"Thermal energy is theoretically presented as random
amplitude distributed over an infinite frequency interval."

I have no idea what that statement means, but I like
the sound of it. Found it in an article on residual noise
in quartz crystals. Don't ask why I was reading an article
on residual noise in quartz crystals. I stumbled on it
while looking for something else. It's like card catalogs.
Remember them? In libraries, prior to computer workstations,
long rows of tiny wooden boxes filled with cards, one
for each book in the library.

Propinquity is why I read the article on quartz crystals
and why I miss card catalogs. I stumbled on hundreds
of fascinating books over the years browsing card catalogs,
discovering Maxine Hong Kingston's *Woman Warrior*
while looking for books by Barbara Kingsolver.

Perhaps randomness is vital to human health, why we dream.
"Random amplitude distributed over an infinite frequency
interval"—sounds like a dream to me. Or life.

"Positing infinity, the rest is easy." Roger Zelazny,
a gifted storyteller and dreamer, said that.
In a world of infinite possibilities anything
might happen, men might understand the needs
of women, and women, men; casual cruelties
disappear, life make sense, love . . .

. . . well, we aren't given infinity, and even
a hundred years, compared to eternity,
might as well be a nanosecond, gone,
a briefly handled card in a small wooden box
in a wall of small wooden boxes that spiral
around a nondescript star, stretching through time
unopened, forgotten—a few scribbled lines, some
numbers, a brief description.

The Zoo Where You're Fed to God

is full of animals, of course,
some in cages, some without.
Most of the animals, both
those in cages and those
who enter the zoo through its large
main gate, are unhappy—this too
is to be expected. All of the animals
are hungry and so too is God, who
in his strolls through the park
occasionally consumes an animal,
leaving behind no remains, no skin
or blood or bone. God is tidy.
If the animal God takes
is one of the caged animals,
all memory of that animal disappears.
If the animal he takes
is one of the uncaged animals,
all memory of that animal disappears.
God is consistent. The animals
in the zoo aren't aware that they exist
as snacks for God, but they're usually
afraid as well as unhappy.
God doesn't understand this
or doesn't care, or perhaps is oblivious.
Sometimes, at the last moment
the animal God has chosen can feel
his invisible approach and trembles.
God smiles then, his breath hot and moist,
and imagines it is like the approach
of a lover's lips.

The Lights in the Sky Are Stars

Stars are different.
They twinkle.
No man-made thing,
no planet does that.
I once knew why
stars twinkle, the scientific
explanation, but I've forgotten.
It doesn't matter.
I'm told they're inanimate.
Still, stars fascinate.
Late at night, alone
as I walk, I think sometimes
the stars are like a flame
deep within me,
tiny, consuming . . .

we are all cripples,
burn with needs
that will one day
use up all we are.
Until that day, we
yearn, caress, whisper
shout and plead,
                    erupt
in great blinding flares
of fire and heat
                    which
to those near us, those we
most long to reach, appear
as light from distant galaxies,
faint and flickering and lost in time.

American Sentences

after Allen Ginsberg

The phone, coiled like an ancient serpent, whispers
vague threats and promises.

Tires grumble through snow, snap chunks of ice, chew
and spit them aside, roll on.

Waves on limestone cliffs, back and forth and back, our words
wearing us away.

Sometimes at night I turn to hold you, find only air,
dream of falling.

In the desert, bright cactus flowers bloom—you touch
my arm, surprise me.

An old man collects cans from trash bins, slips
in and out of shadow, clouds.

The rain has moved east over mountains, trails cirrus
like thin memories.

We arrange and rearrange unspoken words; hope,
like fog, drifts away.

Your face fills my dreams; I wake and the moon is out,
falling through torn clouds.

So cold, stars ache against the taut black sheath
  that prevents their plunge to earth.

TV screens flicker with blue light; from the street
  there is no sound at all.

Snails cross my sidewalk, leave trails I cannot follow;
  I regret each crunch.

And for All the Poets & Writers

& musicians & housewives & students
& bricklayers & builders of houses
& shoe store clerks & dish
washers & waitresses & presidents
of corporations & birdwatchers
& old women who spend their days
pushing stolen grocery carts slowly
down raucous streets & designers of
greeting cards & garbage men &
doctors & lawyers & indigent farmers
& long-distance truckers & cotton
candy vendors & children in love &
beekeepers & angry young men
who stand on moonlit streets
      waiting
for signs from the stars
& grandmothers & grandfathers
& cousins & aunts & brothers
& fathers & mothers & daughters
& the shy freckled girl who sat
at the desk in front of me
in tenth grade
    whose
words & songs & stories
& smiles & anger & fears
& hopelessly awkward loves
& frustrations & laughter
& home-made apple pies &
burnt toast & fumblings
& shinings & futures
were all denied us
because we didn't hear
or see or make an attempt
to understand or offer
to share the pain
that led you
to the knife or rope
or pills or the top

of some silent, concrete-
and-glass altar
                    I wish
I could have been there, not
that I have any answers
but so we could have had
a cup of coffee or taken
a walk along a dusty
canal bank or sung old
rock-and-roll songs
at the moon
or cursed the politicians
or organized a protest march
or climbed the fence to
swim the Montebello pool
at midnight
or just held hands
or touched for a moment
or sat sharing silence
                    long enough
for you to notice your hands
or my hands, and the
intricate, delicate whorls
and patterns that in the right light
appear as parchment or the skin
of lizards whose blood requires
the warmth of the sun.

Wintergreen

I'd never seen anyone with yellow fingertips
like my uncle, Raymond, who chain-smoked Camels
down to nothing. The family didn't talk about it around us kids
but we knew he drank. He'd disappear for months
then one day there he'd be, leaning against a doorway
in his wrinkled green suit and mustard tie, smiling his lopsided
smile, his long fingers dancing in smoke as he told tales
of running hooch in Tennessee, riding the rails, sleeping
in woods with grizzlies and copperheads.

He carried a huge, two-bladed Buck knife that'd slice a tomato
thin as you please. Family rumor was he'd cut a man once,
cut him bad, but I never saw Uncle Raymond angry
or heard him raise his voice above a rough whisper.
He'd stay a few weeks or a few days, then disappear.

He always handed out sticks of Teaberry gum to us kids—
gifts he pretended weren't—said he didn't need 'em,
said he chewed the real thing, leaves right off those bushes.
A guard beat him to death in a Kentucky drunk tank
when I was 12.

Until last fall, I hadn't been to Ohio for twenty years.
I guess being sent halfway round the world put motion
in my blood—I never stopped moving after Vietnam.
In Mansfield, frost had flamed oaks and maples,
the butternut hickories, had begun its slow work
of stripping trees. The city looked old, shabby and alien.

On an early-morning walk through Kingwood Center,
where fog laced the hollows, I stopped at a wintergreen,
the shrub we called teaberry as kids, pulled off a leaf,
held it in my mouth. And there he was again—
Uncle Raymond, that lopsided grin wreathed in smoke,
those cryptic yellow fingers weaving stories, appearing
and disappearing, like leaves falling through fog.

Waiting

It's the standard Monday morning crew
at the unemployment compensation office
taking turns taking numbers:

the middle-aged middle manager
in his three-piece suit, groping
for his new mantra—downsized, downsized

the 55-year-old high-school dropout,
arthritic hands gripping a painfully smeared
application with twelve misspelled words
and three instances of subject/verb disagreement

a surfer who'd rather spend time on his board
off Sunset Cliffs than stacking two-by-fours

the woman who just moved her three kids
back to her parents again

a former Green Beret, needle tracks paralleling
the tattoo of a lightning bolt on his forearm,
trying to recall why he'd punched his foreman.

And I sit on my molded plastic chair
remembering Albert Einstein's quote,
"The great tragedy of life
is what dies in a man while he is alive."

And I watch as a young woman enters the building,
walks to the counter where the red plastic dispenser
sticks out a tiny numbered tongue at her.

And I remember Sam, bleeding out on the floor
of our hooch in Vietnam, face and chest peppered
with shrapnel, whispering *guess I'm going home now.*

And I feel the slight vibrations from the atoms of my chair,
letting go.

12 Pennies

The puzzle was simply stated: 12 pennies, one bad,
either heavy or light; three uses of a balance scale;
find the bad coin; determine if it's heavy or light.

I shouldn't have listened. Brainteasers seize my mind,
chew my consciousness, demand answers. Okay.
Divide the coins into three groups of four. If the first eight
balance, the solution is easy. The odds, however,
suggest imbalance, and I'm down to just two tries.

I pull a penny from my pocket, flip it in the air, catch
it—a mildly tarnished 1987-D, Lincoln's head and shoulders
on one side, his memorial on the reverse. In God We Trust,
Liberty, United States of America, E Pluribus Unum,
One Cent.

It doesn't make sense. Eight coins—two chances to find
the bad one. Why would anyone fake a penny?
It's immaterial. Concentrate. What do I know?

Four good pennies and one of four is heavy or one of four
is light. It's a matter of logic, reasoning, analytic thought.

Okay. If on the second weighing I mix the coins—good
heavy & light—deduce the proper combination . . .

. . . and an hour later, I've found the answer, solved
the puzzle. And I feel such a sense of elation, of passionate
release, I want to tear my clothes off, run screaming
down the street. I grin to myself, as pleased as if I'd won
the Boston Marathon, cured the common cold.

I look at my solution, impressed with its elegance.
And I remember an album my father owned when
I was a child: *With Hearts Aflame* by J.T. Adams
& the Men of Texas, and a song, "The Lost Penny":

"As I was walking down the street
of a little country town,

I saw a rusty penny, half-buried
in the ground. As I bent down
to pick it up, I saw beneath the rust
these words just barely visible,
'In God We Trust' . . ."

It was one of the few albums we owned when I was eight
or nine, and one of my favorite songs. We literally
wore that record out.

Years later I realized the lyrics were untrustworthy,
that pennies don't rust, that God doesn't speak
through lost coins, that life is not a simple puzzle
solved by logic.

And I remember Vietnam, think of my failed marriage,
recall reading that if all the U.S. pennies ever made
were lined up edge to edge, they would circle the earth
137 times, round and round, bright billions
of shining faces—good and bad, heavy
and light—yearning for logic or balance
or absolution.

Headache

I've had the headache for more than a week now.
The first doctor gave me pills. They made me dizzy.

At the hospital, another doctor said inner-ear infection,
gave me more pills. The vertigo went away

when I stopped taking the pills the first doctor gave me.
The headache stayed. It makes me nauseous.

I can't concentrate. I feel awful. I want to see a different
doctor. I've been on hold for more than ten minutes now.

This is the third 800 number I've called, trying to get
CIGNA's permission to change physicians. Someone

is playing a marimba in my head. The musician's not
very good. He's playing the same notes over and over,

insistent, as if he's going to play this tune till he gets it right.
The Muzak on the phone is in a different key, of course.

I want to lie down. I want to vomit. I've just been given
a different 800 number to call and my boss is at my door

with an emergency news-release rewrite. The musician
behind my eyes smiles, blows a smoke ring that

envelops my head and returns to his idiot hammering.
I close my eyes and wait to die.

Seven White Cars

This morning, still rubbing sleep from my eyes
I glance out my bathroom window to check the weather
and immediately forget about clouds and promised rain.
Instead, my mind is seized by the fact that there are
seven white cars parked in a row across the street.
Seven white cars! The rational portion of my brain,
still waking up, immediately flashes me a message:
"It's just coincidence, bub; no big deal"—which I'm sure
is true.

But another part of my brain, the part that
a few minutes earlier had been spinning dreams,
connecting bits and snips of reality with fantasy,
mumbles something about boxcars to heaven,
the purity of white; and my Judeo-Christian upbringing
pipes up with, "Satan is an angel of light," and I think,
"Oh, shut up."

But still, the pattern-finding and meaning-making circuits
in my head (which scientists claim are what really
set us apart from animals, since laughter
and tool making and even the ability to lie
are no longer considered homo sapiens-specific)
keep bugging me with, "Wow, this is very unusual;
this is significant"—which, of course, it isn't. I mean
they're not even the same make and model.
If all seven cars were 1992 white Ford Escorts
with "Vote Republican" stickers on their bumpers,
that would scare me. But they're not.

And it's starting to rain, which means freeway traffic
will be insane, and I'll probably be late for work again.
Cause and effect—that's where significance lies, where
doers doing things constantly change our world.
But it does nothing to explain why love dies, why
things lost can never be recaptured, why the past
is safer than the future, why this morning I feel
an almost overwhelming urge to crawl back under
my covers, to dream.

Life on the Border

"We're going to kill us some niggers and mexicans,"
Carl Havers said, lifting the blanket in his trunk to show me
a .22 rifle, 12-gauge pump shotgun and .38 Smith & Wesson
revolver.

It was 1965 and the smoke from Watts had drifted to Phoenix.
Carl was 15—the same age as me—and stood by the trunk
of his 18-year-old brother's '62 Mercury Comet with its
260 cu. in. V8 and upside-down air cleaner ("because it's
faster that way").

It was Saturday night and the Comet was parked
in front of the bandshell at Encanto Park. "Yeah," said Randy,
Carl's brother, "we're going to blow some greasers away—
wanna come?"

Two weeks earlier my family had been in California
on vacation. In L.A. my father had shown us
where he'd worked in a cookie factory when he was 15.
The next day, while we camped at Pismo Beach,
a hundred and ninety miles to the north, the Watts riots
started on the street we'd walked the day before.

We didn't learn about the riots for two days. We were camping
in a tent near the beach. I met a girl there who told me
she thought I was nice and said she was cold as we walked
together among the dunes; only later did I realize
what she was suggesting, what she really meant.

That summer my uncle was sent to Cleveland
when the Ohio National Guard was mobilized.
They carried riot sticks the size of baseball bats.
One soldier swung his stick like Babe Ruth, leaning
into the stroke as he hit a slow-moving black man
in the back of the head. It sounded, my uncle said,
like a watermelon smacking the sidewalk.

In Arizona, schools were integrated, but there weren't many
black students, and the whites and mexicans pretty much
ignored one another.

"Don't bother with Spanish," a high-school teacher told me.
"German's more practical—much great literature
and science is written in German."

I met Carlos Ramierez Peña in Saigon in 1969. We were
both cherries, fresh in-country, waiting for our permanent
assignments. Over a poker game, we discovered
we'd both grown up in Phoenix. Later, we were assigned
to the same unit. In Vietnam I learned that
whatever the color of your skin, blood is always red.

In 1955 I started first grade in Mansfield, Ohio.
I was five years old. After school one day, I waved
to three black girls walking on the other side of the street
and called, "Hi, niggers." They chased me all the way
home, where I clung to my mother's legs, sobbing
as she told them I was just a little boy and didn't
understand what I'd said—I thought I was being friendly.

I was 23 when I met Angela Reyes. She was 18
and working for the summer at a restaurant
on Central Avenue in Phoenix. She had skin
like creamy cocoa and I tipped her outrageously.
She was the most beautiful woman I'd ever met.
We dated all summer. Her parents were wealthy,
wanted her to attend school back east. She cried
the night she left, but her letters stopped
a few months later, and I never saw her again.

In 1969 I went AWOL from the Army for a week. I rode
with a busload of students to Washington, D.C.,
to protest the war in Vietnam. I stayed in a commune
in a black neighborhood, attended a counter-inaugural
ball in a circus tent next to the Washington monument,
listened to Phil Ochs sing "We Are the Cops of the World,"
burnt my military ID card at a rally. Early one Sunday
morning I walked for hours, watching my breath
make clouds and disappear. The neighborhood
around the commune was quiet and empty.
I encountered only two young black men.
We nodded as we passed.

In the 1978 movie, *The Big Fix*, Richard Dreyfus plays
a former anti-war activist turned private eye. In one scene
he sits in a film library watching newsreels of the 60s
peace movement, tears streaming down his face.

In 1959, on a tour of the Heard Museum where Navajo
Indians were displaying cultural artifacts and performing
native dances, Mrs. Grandell cautioned our fourth-grade
class, "Enjoy their authentic presentations, but don't go
too near the Indians—they have lice in their hair."

In 1981 I moved to British Columbia, Canada.
On a weekend in Vancouver, I bought a ticket
for *Superman II*. In the final scene of the movie,
after defeating evil aliens, Superman flew the American flag
to the top of the White House. As the camera zoomed in
on a close-up of Superman and the Stars and Stripes,
half of the audience booed.

In August 1968 I had just finished basic training,
had been accepted for the Special Forces.
I was going to be a Green Beret. On a Sunday afternoon
I was sitting on the steps of our barracks reading a novel.
My platoon sergeant came out of the company headquarters
whistling energetically as he walked toward me. He seemed
in a good mood. "Whatchu readin', troop," he asked.
I showed him the cover of *A Canticle for Liebowitz*.
He looked at it for a moment, then frowned and said,
"Son, we don't read that kinda stuff 'round here.
That useless shit will just fuck up your mind."

On a Friday night in 1991 I stood on a sidewalk
in downtown San Diego with a small group of protestors,
holding a sign that read "Vietnam Veteran Against the War."
Across the street, a much larger group of counter-protestors
waved flags and carried signs that read "Free Kuwait"
& "Nuke 'Em Till They Glow." A young man in a Navy uniform
ran across the street and spit at my face, yelling
"What were you, you coward, a fucking cook?"

In December 1970, ten days before I turned twenty-one,
I stood at the entrance of Richland Mall in Mansfield, Ohio,

looking at all the bright colors, dazed.
Forty-eight hours earlier I had been in Vietnam.
I was wearing a pair of my younger brother's shoes,
a size and a half too large, because I didn't have
any civilian shoes that fit and I refused to wear
my jump boots. All the bright colors—that's the only thing
I remember from my first month home.

In 1965 in Phoenix I stood looking at a trunk full of guns,
thinking of the stark, black-and-white TV images
of Los Angeles burning. I wanted to hold a rifle
in my hands, be John Wayne, blast the bad guys.
Instead, I watched as the Havers brothers
burned rubber leaving the park, then sat on a hill
above the bandstand and stared at the moon
rising behind Camelback Mountain, orange
and swollen, and thought about the girl
on Pismo Beach.

War

Saying Goodbye, 1969

We met early for breakfast,
sausage and eggs half eaten.

At North Lake Park, we scuffed
through leaves, trees appearing

and disappearing as fog whorled
the hollows, bird calls faint and

echoey, thin as our shadows
or the sunlight that October

morning I left for the war:
chalk on eggshell.

Interstices

I once killed a truck and a tree—not on the same day
of course. I killed the tree first. The truck came much later.
I killed the tree because I was 19, and scared.
I had been in Vietnam 12 days and it was my third night
on perimeter guard. I didn't mean to kill the tree—it was
an accident. I've always liked trees. It was a small tree
about 40 yards from our perimeter wire, and at three o'clock
that morning, it started moving toward me, so I shot it.
Several times. The lieutenant wasn't happy.

I killed the truck almost a year later. It wasn't an accident.
The truck had broken down on Highway 1 about a quarter
klick from our base camp. It got dark before they got it fixed,
so they had to leave it sitting, and later that night
I got an M-79 grenade launcher and blew it up.
I blew it up because I was angry. I was angry
because my friend, Tessler, had died that morning.
He had died when the deuce-and-a-half he was driving
had been blown off the road by a Claymore mine
and he had been pinned in the cab, and the truck had caught
fire, and it happened so fast there was nothing anyone
could do—and Tessler had been going home in four days.
I'm sorry about the tree.

First Light

The night is thick with yearnings,
sweat so raw and viscous
it nails flesh to sheets.

These Saigon barracks reek of piss
and fear, cup the real and imagined
goblins of 19-year-old boys whose
ears, like soft wax seashells, still
shine pink with adolescence—boys
who've come from Omaha and
Columbus, from Oakland and Phoenix,
children of Humpty Dumpty and Roy
Rogers, sons of John Wayne and
Elmer Fudd, through whose dreams
a demented cowboy wails a song
of *indian country*, of punji sticks
and trip wires and tiny black-clad VC
with teeth so large they eat the sky
and laugh with flaming tongues
that swallow stars.

And in the morning
the sky surprises: blue
as calm as painted china,
patient as a hat—the sun
warm and yellow as butter
or dandelions
or the hair of a girl
whose kiss one summer evening
tasted of strawberries.

A Vietnam Alphabet

A is for America. It's funny the things we do for love.

B is for bombs. B-52s dropped thousands of bombs
on Vietnam—they tore up a lot of ground.
Bouncing Betties were small, anti-personnel bombs
used in ambushes. One blew the legs off a friend of mine.

C is for Charlie, the Viet Cong. They thought we were
invading their country.

D is for dead.

E is for E-1, E-2, E-3, etc. Those are Army ranks.
The higher the number, the less chance you'd fall
under "D".

F is for the first letter of the English word used most often
in Vietnam.

G is for grunt, also known as 11-bang-bang, also known as
infantryman, also known as expendable.

H is for Home, the World.

I is for in-country, in Vietnam, "indian country"—as if
this were some kind of John Wayne movie.
"I" is also for inane, insane.

J is for jungle.

K is for kill.

L is for loneliness.

M is for Medevac. Those were the helicopters
that flew you out if you were wounded. Or dead.

N is for nothing.

O is for officers. They often knew nothing.

P is for peace. It goes well with

Q which is for quiet. For years after I came home,
too much peace and quiet would make me nervous.

R is for R & R: rest & recuperation, rest & relaxation,
rest & return.

S is for shrapnel. Sam, who slept in the bunk next to mine,
stopped a piece of shrapnel with his heart one night.

T is for Time. DEROS. Date of Estimated Return from Overseas. Each of us knew the exact number of days left in-country. No more and (we hoped) no less.

U is for us-versus-them. Which wasn't always clear. *We have met the enemy*, Pogo said, *and he is us.*

V is for victory. Or at least peace with honor. Or at least going home.

W is for words. Vietnam was not a war. It was a police action. Does that sound more civilized? Does that make it moral? Do we use words or do words use us?

X is for external. Some veterans came home with external scars. Many others came home with no scars. Externally.

Y is for yesterday. Or maybe tomorrow. There is no **Z**. Some things have no end.

A is for anger.

B is for bitterness.

C is for . . .

John Wayne Hardly Ever Died

That's what he remembered from his childhood: vivid scenes
of magnificent galloping horses and six-shooters
that occasionally held more than six shots.
And that craggy profile, caught in the camera's lens,
turned half toward his friends, half toward some cunningly
dangerous but conquerable foe, exhorting his men to never
give up, never give in—to fight that good fight, to kill the indians
or outlaws or mexicans or germans or japanese or communists
or anyone who threatened our way of life, our glorious freedom.

That's what he remembered when at 18 he volunteered
for the draft, crawled through acres of mud, swung from ropes
and chains, shot and stabbed and maimed, learning the arts
of war—ran for miles, jumped out of planes, ate goats
and snakes, won his Green Beret:

John Wayne, standing tall, the light of the setting sun
illuminating his face, its lines and pain, his fierce grief
over the death of a soldier and friend, but also
his determination not-to-let-that-death-be-in-vain.

Later, he realized that Wayne, facing the sun as it set
into the South China Sea off the coast of Vietnam,
was looking east. The sun had set in the east!
It was make-believe—all smoke and mirrors
and sleight of hand—illusion.

That's what he remembered as he lay against
a rice paddy berm in South Vietnam, holding a friend
whose breath grew ragged and slow as the hole in his chest
sputtered and blew small bubbles of blood that went pop,
pop, pop, like some silly children's toy.

Year's End

When I was twenty I lost Christmas. I remember
New Year's well enough. At midnight the perimeter,
despite all orders to the contrary, lit up with red,
green and white flares while tracer rounds from M-60
machine guns wove graceful red arabesques in the sky.

But Christmas is gone. It's like trying to remember
your ninth grade algebra teacher, the one you got
an "F" from—Mrs. Alister. You know her name
because you found the report card, buried for 27 years
in a box of papers you lugged through every move
but opened only when the basement flooded this spring.
You know her name, but there's no face, no body,
no memory.

That's how my Christmas is. I know there was one.
I know I was there. But that's all.

Other Christmases are fine: At five, my brother
and I, wearing matching cowboy pajamas with painted
six-guns on the hips, watching the Mickey Mouse Club
on Christmas Eve.

In Ohio, that snowman as tall as my Dad, and later
in Arizona, a Christmas Eve picnic on South Mountain
in shirt sleeves and shorts, the air so clear
it seemed you could see the future.

And at 11, my father's job as a bricklayer lost
to a broken scaffolding, a ruptured disc—my mother
working nights at Woolworth's. That was the year
a shredded tire ten miles from home took their last
ten dollars, and my brother and I scoured the neighborhood
for bottles, proudly bringing home milk and bread for supper.
It was a wonderful Christmas.

And at 15, Vicki Wright and I playing Mary and Joseph
in the church Christmas pageant, my fake beard
itching like crazy. Later, behind the church,
we kissed for the first time.

Even now that memory is as clear as the water
that rushed down Rum Creek the Christmas
we spent at Big Bear, snow high on both banks,
the pebbles in the streambed as bright
and distinct as if there were no water at all.

In Vietnam I lost Christmas. At firebase Jack,
north of Hue, in 1969.

Booby Trap

He breathes through his mouth
avoiding the bitter-spice smell
of gunfire and flesh—eyes
unfocused as he leans against a wall,
wiping at the blood drying on his shirt.

Now, with hesitant fingers
he probes the swelling
under his right eye,
still seeing brilliant spotted
flashes of red and green,
and waits for the medic,
not thinking, thinking . . .

three days, then sends us back out
picking up ammo cans
left there
empty
three days . . .

his eye swelling shut
where his friend's head,
a bright flower blooming,
had seeded the air
with pieces of skull.

The Night of the Day that Davey Maxwell Died

The night of the day that Davey Maxwell died
I sat in the sandy courtyard formed by the five gray hooches
of our compound and listened to rock-and-roll songs
and watched the moon. The moon was full and bright
with the sharp, fragile clarity that is only seen far from cities,
a clarity too gentle and serene to have come from the sun—
but it had.

The sun. Giver of life, bringer of death. They say the sun
kills us, ages us, cuts short the Methuselan span
that should be ours. Some say the earth before the Flood
was sheathed in clouds, clouds that gentled the sun's
intemperate gifts and granted long years. But Noah's voyage
marked an end to that gift—God's wrath leaving Time
ten times more our enemy.

It seemed odd that night, sitting in my chair, listening
to the Beatles, to feel such peace after seeing Davey
die that morning. The music seemed to rise, drawn
by the mild night wind, to float above my head
before softly drifting off to wherever it is music goes
after dancing the tiny bones of our inner ears.

I sat, suspended by a thread that stretched from the past
(from a place we called "the World," as if where we were
was just an illusion, a dream from which we would
soon awake to find ourselves home). I sat clutching
that thread, linked to the past through the slowly
spinning hubs of my cassette player, enveloped
in the familiar cocoon of the music.

My father hated my music, had in fact once smashed
my entire collection of 45s, furious that I would buy such trash
and hide it in my room. Yet he had sat, patiently—for hours—
recording that music, each record, each side, to send
to his son in Vietnam. I think I've never loved my father more
than when I received those tapes.

Davey never knew his father. His parents were divorced
when he was three. He had been in-country
just two months. He was like some large puppy,
friendly and eager, ready to try anything to please.
We called him Sunshine.

We were returning from a long, fruitless
night reconnaissance, the sun just breaking the horizon
when a single shot knocked Davey to the ground.
Our return fire shredded leaves and branches
and was swallowed by the jungle. And then silence.
For twenty seconds the only sounds were the slight rasps
of canvas on cloth, an occasional metallic clink
as someone shifted position, the sighs of broken foliage
slipping toward the ground, a breath of bluish smoke.
Then a bird trilled, and another; insects returned
and our squad unfroze.

Davey lay where he had been thrown by the bullet
that tore off half his face. We never found the sniper. . . .

I sat in our compound all night that night playing my tapes
again and again, watching the moon slowly cross the sky:
beautiful, distant, invincible. The sunrise that morning
was the most beautiful I think I've ever seen, clouds
resting like islands above the sea, their colors fiery
yet delicate. The sunrise filled me with joy—how strange,
the sun.

The Way of the Snake

The snake had made its home in an old bunker
we had been assigned to clean out. Finding it,
we had stopped, debated what to do. And because
I was in charge of the detail, the decision fell to me.
For half an hour or more we tried to coax the python
(for as we later discovered, it was a regal python)
out of its adopted home. It almost became a game for us,
trying to lure the python out, jumping back when it moved
too close, laughing at our own nervous fear.

Then Lt. Hassler, the Officer of the Day, arrived
to check our progress and was apprised of the situation.
Quit screwing around, he said, *just blow the sucker away.*
Well, sir, I replied, *I think with a little more time . . .*

We haven't got more time, he snapped.
I want that bunker operational before dark.

When the lieutenant had left, we stood for a moment
staring at the ground, each of us unwilling to look
into the others' eyes. *Shit*, I finally mumbled
and grabbed my rifle and a flashlight and turned back
toward the bunker.

Although there was still an hour of daylight left,
the bunker was already dark, its interior crossed
by long shadows. I entered cautiously, not sure
if the snake had moved, holding the flashlight
next to the barrel of my M-16, sweeping the floor
with its bright beam of light. The snake was still there
lying coil upon coil upon coil. It lifted its head, tongue
sliding lazily out, testing the air. I pulled back the bolt
on my M-16 and let it snap forward, loading a round
into the chamber. I had never shot a snake before.
I set my weapon on full automatic
and took another step forward.

Sorry, snake, I said. The short burst, in the beam
of the flashlight, almost appeared to strike the snake
in slow motion, its head sliding backward, separating

from its body, the body twisting slowly with the impacts,
neatly stacked coils looping in confusion, jerked
spasmodically by bullets ripping through its flesh.

Afterwards, as we dragged the pieces out,
I said nothing, but I felt a great pressure
as if a hand were squeezing my heart.

I saw another snake die that year. But it was
a different kind of snake: man-made. The Huey Cobra
had been flying close support that night
and was just overhead when a rocket
smashed it from the sky. And in that fire-filled instant
I watched as the chopper tumbled toward the ground,
folding slowly in on itself, like the slow-motion blooming
of a rose filmed in reverse, crushed in the earth's
awkward embrace, jerking convulsively as flames
ate through its flesh.

The Encyclopedia Americana has this to say under the
heading of python:

> *The regal python (python reticulatus)*
> *of southeast Asia is primarily nocturnal*
> *in its habits, feeding largely on small*
> *mammals and birds. Its constricting powers*
> *are much exaggerated. The victim is killed*
> *by pressure on the heart and lungs, not*
> *by crushing. Bones are rarely broken,*
> *nor is the skin bruised.*

just squeeze

it was gonna be his ticket home just a flesh wound you know like those TV detectives always got a clean hole punched through soft tissue no veins no arteries no real damage but enough to take him to the rear some base hospital with pretty nurses and a real bed with sheets hot food hot water maybe even a bathtub soak them humpin'-the-boonies blues away had it all figured out wait till almost dark sittin' on the edge of his foxhole cleaning rag out weapon pointed down muzzle near his calf say it went off accidental while he was tryin' to figure why it'd been jammin' everybody knew M-16s jammed just point and squeeze sure it'd hurt a little but it'd be better than waitin' for Charlie to put one through his head that would happen soon he'd dreamed it some sniper sightin' down the back of his brain ready to turn his skull into some kinda Humpty Dumpty jigsaw puzzle pieces scattered like bloody egg shell all over a rice paddy berm this was better just exhale and squeeze real soft blam clean little hole and home free nobody could expect him to go humpin' a rucksack with a hole through his leg at the least he'd get assigned to the rear limp real good for a few months till he was so short it wouldn't matter maybe it'd be better if he closed his eyes come on you're not gonna make it out here you know it just do it think of that nice tub of steamin' water sweet-smellin' Ivory soap home just squeeze

Waiting on Ambush with My Best Friend Ray

Bound by jungle, wedge of sky, we lay out
lines of fire—check claymores, set trip wires, wait.

Our patch of sky is blue and blue and now
perhaps, a profounder arc of blue, as

Ray brushes my arm with his fingertips,
points to a nearby branch, a small green frog,

throat sac pulsing in & out, bulbous toes
tiny and fierce where they grip the bark, eyes

so black they devour the light, turning day
to night, its great throat throbbing in & out

and one by one, exhaled, the stars appear.

Napalm

The boy wears only a pale green shirt,
no pants or shorts or shoes—a six-year-old,
fat stick in hand, squatting in the dirt.

He glances up as our convoy passes,
eyes dark and blank, and shifts his weight
to favor his left leg, ridges of scar
from ankle to hip twisted and shiny as plastic.

Yellow dust, kicked up by our trucks
hangs in the air, thick and choking.
But the boy, face calm as a cat, just stares,
only his eyelids moving, up and down
up and down. Finally, he looks away and
raising his club, resumes his task,
pounding ants.

At Phu Loc

Smoke from the burning rose slowly, as if reluctant
to depart, or as if gravity were suddenly more insistent
on that spot.

The air filled with a mist of ash which, settling, leached
all color from the earth, absorbed green and blue, ate
yellow like a monkey, layered red to pink to a hue
so pale it hurt the eyes.

And still the flames curled and choked, burst bright
for moments, then hid, crawled through gray twilight
that cloaked the sun and turned summer suddenly cool,
hinted of far Octobers and gibbous moons, full and low,
of fat buckeye rosaries and pungent leaves raked
into piles over and over—and the fragrance at night
when for blocks in all directions smoke would rise
from backyard autumn fires.

And the stinging in my eyes was from the ash of the fire
and from what was lost to the fire
and from what is always lost to the fire
and from what is always lost
and the fire.

October 1969

Autumn feels free. It always has. Why this should be
I don't know. There's always this feeling of abandon,
of celebration, like being fired from a job you hate.

October 1969 was the freest moment of my life.
But it wasn't the only autumn that was special to me.
They all were as far back as I can remember. In autumn
I could breathe. The cold cleared my sinuses, unblocked
passages and I could breathe.

And as a child I felt the magic—in the smoky air at night,
in the carefree falling leaves, in the way bricks sat in walls
so red and neat; my father was a bricklayer and my mother
told me stories about his work: of laughing bricks who laid
themselves and ate mortar like cream cheese.

The magic was real and it came in autumn. On Halloween
we ran from house to house, ghostly sheets white
and flapping, ethereal in our joy. And later, our bags
would erupt on the kitchen table, spill onto the floor
a million different candies, all bright and beckoning.

But October 1969 was the freest moment of my life.
With orders for Vietnam, I was given four weeks' leave.
I went home to north-central Ohio. For a month I cruised
the streets. I walked and sat and looked at things.
I was memorizing my life—not consciously, but memorizing
nonetheless. Only now, 20 years later, do I recognize
what I was doing that month. I was preparing to die.

I laughed a lot. I drove up and down Lexington Avenue
a dozen times a day, honking my horn, waving at people
for no reason. I spent hours at Kingwood Center
among the wild, familiar trees, watching the leaves
release and fall. I stood across the street from the shop
where an old girlfriend worked, watched her climb
a ladder to pull a blanket down from a high shelf.
She was wearing a blue skirt with slash pockets
and a white V-neck sweater.

Even the songs they played on the radio that month
are still bright for me, still tingle. Even the silly bubble-gum
songs: "Tracy, when I'm with you, something you do
bounces me off the ceiling . . ."

The leaves are falling again. The sky is low and gray.
The air is crisp enough that a deep breath
is almost painful. Autumn feels free.

The Monkey Gourd

Blake laughed, grimaced and coughed. From the corner
of his mouth a thin stream of blood trickled down his chin,
turning the already-damp collar of his olive-drab jungle
fatigues even darker.

"It's the damn monkey gourd," he said, and laughed again,
clenching his teeth on the pain. "Hey Cramer, you listenin'?"
He carefully turned his head to the left and squinted
at Cramer, who lay a few feet away, eyes closed, mouth
open, breathing in shallow ragged breaths.

"Damn you, Cramer. Don't you die on me you dumb farmer—
the dust-off's comin'." Blake glanced at the tourniquet
he had tied just above Cramer's knees, just above
the splintered bone and raw meat that had been
Cramer's legs. "You hold on Cramer, just hold on."

Blake coughed again and almost passed out
from the sharp pain in his right side. "Oh man!
I think all my ribs are busted. Where's the damn slicks?"

He checked his M-16 again, making sure he'd put a fresh clip
in, even though the firefight had moved off, had become
a distant series of isolated pops and brief bursts, and finally
had been completely swallowed by the jungle.

He allowed his eyes to slowly close then quickly
forced them open again—that's no good. "Hey Cramer,"
he said, remembering what he had been going to say.
"You ever hear how they catch monkeys in Africa?
They get these gourds and put some nuts or something
in them and tie 'em to a tree. Then some dumb monkey
comes along, sticks his fist in the gourd to get the nuts
and gets stuck 'cause he can't pull his fist out with the nuts
in it. If he'd just let go of the nuts, he could get his hand out
and escape. But he's too greedy and dumb to do that,
so *poof!* monkey stew."

He glanced at Cramer again who gave no sign
that he'd heard. "A bunch of dumb monkeys,"
Blake said. "Too stupid to open their fists and lose
the nuts—WHERE'S THE FUCKING DUST-OFF!"
his voice cracking, fresh blood covering his lower lip
and chin.

Blake lay very still for several minutes breathing slowly
through his mouth, eyes half closed. "Had a girlfriend
once," he finally said. "God, I loved that woman.
But she'd been married to a real jerk. She'd idolized him
and he'd played around on her. And afterwards
she just wouldn't let go of the fear, swore she'd never
be hurt like that again. Wish I'd gotten through
to her—I really tried. God, I loved that woman."

He glanced at his friend again. "Hey Cramer! Hold on,
man. That slick's comin'. Hold tight." Another coughing fit
blanked out Blake's vision for a moment and afterwards,
his voice was almost a whisper: "Dumb monkeys.
Dumb greedy little monkeys. Hey Cramer, you hang in
there, buddy. That dust-off's comin'. It's comin' soon.
Just hold on—hold on. . . ."

And Giants in the Land

He stood 5'10"—the average height for North American
males. But that day, moving through the Vietnamese hamlet,
he felt gigantic, swollen and angry, head and shoulders above
the frightened peasants who fled from his eyes,
the hard angles of his shoulders, the stench of reptile
that lay coiled and hungry in his brain, older and far
stronger than logic.

And as he let the bolt of his M-16 slam forward,
the cave of his eyes swallowed the light
in a whisper of claws, a dark glinting of scales.

And afterwards, even years afterwards,
what forced him to the top of skyscrapers,
poised for flight, or left him curled
in dark, wet corners
was not the horror
but memory of the fierce, hot joy.

Just Like in the Movies

Bobo's a noisy drunk. He's sure some swinging dick
back in the World is screwing his wife, that although
he has only 37 days left in-country he's going to get
zapped any day now, that the Army's never going
to let him go, that gravity's an illusion, that the earth
sucks.

Tonight, he's moaning and groaning and tossing
on his bunk like a toy sailboat in wild seas. Suddenly
he screams, "It's snowing like a motherfucker in here!"
and rolls off his bunk with a thud that jerks Sergeant
Packner to his feet, fumbling for his steel pot and rifle,
wide-eyed from his dreams.

"What the fuck!" Packner stares around the hooch,
ready to leap for the floor or door, whichever seems
most prudent. Bobo sits up on the wooden floor, legs
stretched out in front of him like a 3-year-old, upper body
weaving from side to side, and yells again, "It's snowing
like a motherfucker in here!"

All five of Bobo's hooch-mates are awake now. "Jesus,"
says Spec/4 LaDeux, flipping a switch that illuminates
the hooch with light from a single 100-watt bulb that
hangs from the central roof beam. "Can't somebody shut
Bobo up?" PFC Sawyer lights a cigarette, snapping his
Zippo closed with a practiced flip of his wrist. "Fucking
clown." Sergeant Gomez scratches his head, looks
at Bobo, then turns toward the wall and pulls his blanket
over his head.

"It's snowing, it's snowing," Bobo cackles, then chokes
momentarily on his own spit.

"Come on, Bobo," says PFC Washington, slipping
his arms under Bobo's and hoisting him to his feet.
"Back to bed."

"Ha ha," says Bobo, and as Washington lowers him
to a sitting position on his bunk, Bobo slumps over

and vomits on Washington's bare legs and feet. "Fuck,"
says Washington, jumping back. Bobo sways on his bunk,
spittle hanging like a doily from his chin, his eyes unfocused,
face vacant. "Fuck," says Washington again, and stomps
out of the hooch.

"Ho ha," says Bobo, and belches loudly, absently scratching
at his belly.

"I'm going to knock his face off," says Packner, striding over
to Bobo, fist half-cocked. Then he stops and grins at LaDeux.
"What you wanna bet I can knock him out with one punch?"

"Twenty bucks," says Sawyer from the other side of the room,
swinging his legs over the side of his bunk, alert now
to the possibility of some action. "One punch
and he has to be out cold."

Packner rubs his chin, then shakes his arms, loosening up.
Packner is tall, with a small waist that widens rapidly
to a broad chest. His arms are powerful, biceps chiseled
and massive. He flexes his pecs. "Somebody's got to
hold him up so's I get a good angle," he says, eyeing Bobo's
chin critically.

"Jesus, Packner," says LaDeux, "what's with this John Wayne
shit? Just stick some cotton in your ears."

"Fuck you, Doodoo," says Packner, warming up to his idea.
"Come on, Sawyer, help me stand him up."

With Sawyer's help, Packner gets Bobo to his feet. He tilts
Bobo's chin up slightly. "Now hold still, Bobo," he says,
grinning. "This'll hurt me more than it'll hurt you."

"Hey, buddy," says Bobo, squinting at Packner.

"If you're going to do it," says Sawyer, "do it—one punch,
out cold."

Gomez has pulled his blanket back down and is sitting up
watching the proceedings with interest. Even LaDeux, despite
his low tolerance for macho men, looks intrigued.

"You ever done this kinda thing before, Packner?
You're not gonna really hurt him, right?"

"Don't sweat it, man—just check this out." He tilts
Bobo's chin up again. Bobo smiles sleepily and belches.
"Sweet dreams, baby," says Packner, and throws
the punch, a quick jab that snaps Bobo's head sharply
to the right.

Bobo's eyes cross and LaDeux steps forward, prepared
to help Sawyer break the fall. But Bobo doesn't fall.
He shakes his head slowly, then looks at Packner,
confusion on his face. "Why'd you hit me?" he asks.
"Why'd you do that?" fat tears sliding from the corners
of his eyes. Bobo backs up a step and sits down hard
on his bunk. He begins to sob—loud, harsh wails
that shake his whole body. "Why'd you hit me?" he cries.

LaDeux turns away in disgust. Sawyer smiles at Packner.
"You owe me $20, man." Gomez snorts and lies back
down. Packner is shaking his hand, flexing his fingers.
The knuckle at the base of his middle finger is already
beginning to swell. "Shit, man, I think I hurt myself."

Bobo has stopped crying and is looking around the hooch,
puzzled. He wiggles his toes and tries unsuccessfully
to focus on them, then frowns and flops back down
on his bunk. LaDeux flips the light off.

Packner sits on the edge of his cot, shoulders slumped,
staring at his hand. Half an hour later, he still can't sleep,
listens to the 105s from the artillery unit on the other side
of the camp firing H&I into the jungle. His hand throbs,
middle knuckle the size of a walnut. "Fuck, man,"
he mutters to himself, "it sure looks easier than that
in the movies."

Across the room, Bobo rolls over in his sleep.
"It's snowing, it's snowing," he yells.

Number 149*

for Jeffrey Charles Davis

"the ugliest thing. . ."
long narrow box
black granite slabs
thick shadows
shot with green
arm patch
Screaming Eagle
hard eyes bright
with chains
that tinkle
like thin silver bells
Da Nang Pleiku Chu Lai
smoked green flowers
and seas—greengreen emeralds
sharp hard flowers
to decorate
years in D.C.
policeofficerwifechildren
fingers numb from readings
caressing granite
namesnames sinking
to ocean depths
octopi dreams
and the red stretched
tissues thrum
he said: "the ugliest
thing I ever saw"
a pull more grim
than gravity
down green jungle streams
of trees and leaves
swollen falling
putrefied: the trigger
softer than granite.

* The Vietnam War Memorial in Washington, D.C., is made of
148 granite slabs. Jeffrey Davis, a Vietnam veteran, killed
himself there.

A Quarter to Wash, the Dry Is Free

It's just that they surprised me.
It had been almost five years, and I normally
wouldn't have reacted like that—but I was alone

in the laundromat, late on a Saturday night,
watching my clothes spin round.
It probably would have been OK, though,

if my back hadn't been to the door, and if
I hadn't been half-asleep, sitting
on a table, hypnotized

by the kaleidoscopic spinning of the dryer.
But I was, and it was, and when the three
tiny women entered the laundromat, speaking

rapidly in Vietnamese, I leaped to the floor
and spun, crouched, my fingers spread wide
and tensed. For an instant,

we stood frozen, like a carefully posed
photograph, then, slowly, I relaxed
and pulling my still-damp clothes

from the dryer, I fled—but they knew—
in their bright, watching eyes
I saw they knew.

Swap Meet

The pale green tile walls of the swap-meet men's room
smelled faintly of antiseptic and strongly of urine.
After the bright, hot light of the Arizona afternoon
the room seemed cave-like.

The door to the first stall was missing and an old wheelchair
sat, half-in, half-out, the fake-leather vinyl of its seat
cracked and peeling, a shade of green just slightly darker
than the bathroom walls.

The man was on the floor, sweat running jaggedly
in the deep cracks and lines of his face as he silently
struggled to lift himself to the toilet seat. He had no legs.
I stood for a moment watching, then stepped forward
to offer help. His arms were long and, unmistakably,
had once been arms of great strength, his clothes
those of a vagrant, their colors all merging, inevitably,
toward a dull greenish-gray.

And as he wrapped his long arms around me and I lifted him,
the smell took me back to the dark green matted wall of jungle
and fatigues worn day after day through torrential rains
and mud and sweat and fear. And as I waited for him,
I remembered. And as I left that men's room after helping
the old man back into his wheelchair, back into the sun-bright
afternoon, I wondered why I felt such shame.

Windows
November 2000

For 29 years I've kept the blinds on my windows closed
at night. When I was married, I told my wife I liked
our privacy, didn't want people walking by looking in.
I lied.

But all this time I didn't know I'd lied, until today. Today
the ex-wife of another vet wrote me of her husband's fear
of leaving the blinds open at night, how it took him
15 years to tell her how dark the nights in Nam were,
how if you lit a match you were a sitting target, how
a lit window left him wide open and exposed to the world.

And I sat there after reading her e-mail, stunned.
How could I not know? After all these years, after
all the poems and stories, the introspection
and sleepless nights, the 3 a.m. walks and hundreds
of books I've read, trying to understand . . .

. . . *wide open and exposed to the world.*

Buffalo

for Brian Willson*

They fired until no ammunition remained, until their fingers
ached and the barrels of their carbines grew too hot
to touch—and still the herd ran on, its dust obscuring the sun,
forcing passengers to squint and rub their eyes.

In one day alone they killed 10,000 buffalo, shooting
from the train as it rolled on new rails, bright against
raw black earth, corpses left where they had fallen, bloated,
stinking in the sun; and the train never slowed, belched
inexorably west, leaving in its wake 10,000 dark mounds
like droppings.

On the hills above the plain a small band of Arapaho
watched the slaughter, watched an enemy whose medicine
was too strong for arrows or knives. And later they sang
their death chant, and their blood and salt soaked the earth
where they died.

And a century later the slaughter continues, and the blood
and salt and bone of turtles and elk, gophers and bear,
women and children and men of all colors soak the earth
while the ghosts of ten million buffalo wait and missiles fly
and automatic weapons bark and the earth turns
like a poisoned coyote, frothing and mad, in circles
ever tighter and tighter.

* Brian Willson, a Vietnam veteran, lost his legs while protesting
U.S. arms shipments to Central America when the train
carrying the arms failed to stop for protesters on the tracks.

September 25, 2001

I'll be sitting somewhere, a restaurant say,
eating lunch, when for no apparent reason
my throat tightens, vision blurs and an almost
unbearable sense of sadness turns
my bones leaden.

And I see that second plane
again—so swift—intersecting
the World Trade tower. It's like some
third-rate action film, the explosion, fire
and smoke, and later the collapse, first one

then the other. And I hear the wife of one of the
passengers on the plane that went down
in Pennsylvania, her last conversation with
her husband, who said, "Some of us
are going to try to do something."

And I feel the thump of mortar rounds, feet
scrambling, screams—*incoming!*—icy rush
of adrenaline transforming reality, my 19-year-old
skin flush with animal fear. And 32 years later,

a sudden hollowness in my chest and I see again
the bombed out temple in Vietnam, ruins of a wall,
thick green vines clutching a shattered pillar,
a small boy wearing only an electric-blue velvet shirt
running down a dusty trail, disappearing

into the jungle. And I'm torn by love for my country,
fear for my country, fear for those nameless
Afghani refugees piled like stones against
the Pakistani border, borders of all sizes and shapes
like bands of steel crossing my chest.

I try to get away—a motorcycle trip to the mountains
last weekend, fast twisting roads, air crisp and clear,
western white pines the green of crayons
pasted against a sky so blue
my eyes ache, remembering.

An Epitaph
October 1983

A friend of mine died the other day,
but not really—I mean it wasn't really
the other day. It just seems that way sometimes.
Sometimes the thirteen years seem a day
and I hold him in my arms again and watch
the warmth and gentleness and intelligence
fade slowly from his eyes while I tell him
everything will be okay, everything will be okay.

I was a writer even then, but none of the words I knew
could stop his blood from seeping through my shirt
to turn its olive drab a darker hue than red
or green—none of the important or subtle
or achingly beautiful words could grant another breath
or give me time to say the things I should have
or would have, but didn't.

There was an accident the other day.
A car had left the road and a passenger was trapped,
held, the driver pleading in a soft, frightened voice:
everything will be okay, won't it?—everything
will be okay?

Oh, the words, the words,
the achingly inadequate beautiful words.

Love

In the Clouds, the Sun

That Monday morning in 1972 the newspaper carried
a color photograph on the front page—it was that unusual.
And although the photo was spectacular, it was like
telling someone who's lived their entire life in Oklahoma
the ocean is large and blue and flatter than any plain—
that inadequate.

Sunday, late in the afternoon, I'd walked into the kitchen
to get a Coke and had stopped, amazed. The air outside
my kitchen window was pink—no, not pink, but rose
or salmon, a color I'd never seen before, a color the sky
had never been before—and I hurried to the door
then slowly moved outside into the heart of a pale
red jewel, air sparking crimson, almost glowing,
and for a moment I could not breathe.

My neighbors stood in the middle of the street, looking
east, heads tilted back, mouths open. Up and down the
block, doors opened, people rushed out, then stopped or
moved as if underwater or in a dream, transfixed
by the clouds.

The clouds filled the eastern sky like some Himalayan
basket of carnations, flowering impossibly high,
the bright blue of the sky behind them in sharp contrast
to their fairy-tale hues of red and pink, carmine
and claret, vermilion, coral, ruby and scarlet.

There was no breeze and the trees seemed etched
in pale fire, each leaf straining for release yet strangely
calm, as if a long wait were over. No cars moved, insects
were silent, no birds flew—and for long minutes
the entire street seemed to hold its breath. . . .

And sometimes in the morning, when we stand
at the bathroom counter together and I watch you
in the mirror, drying your hair or massaging a kink
from your neck, I catch a glimpse of a color
I've never seen before, and for a moment
cannot breathe.

Honeymoon — The First Day

I remember most the light, Dana Point
that early Sunday morning, pristine air

lucent with dew. At an outdoor café
fruit platters ripe with scents, aromatic

arbors thrust fresh and dripping from the sea.
Even the street names glowing—Red Lantern

Golden Lantern—and you: mouth full, elbows
on the table, hands hiding your smile, eyes

so full of light I feared sparks would ignite
the umbrella above us—Rebecca.

Passages

My wife sits on the waterbed in the middle of our bedroom,
propped up by four pillows. Books, papers, and marking pens
in fluorescent yellow, blue and green surround her.
She is studying law, as she does most nights and weekends.
She'll graduate in June. It's 9:00 p.m. I've just come home,
gone fourteen hours today. *Are you happy, Rebecca?*

I want to take your book away, touch your hair. I want us
to sing old rock-and-roll songs together like we used to.
Instead, I peck your cheek. You grunt *hello*, return
to your studies. I drop my book bag by the closet door,
remove my shoes, enter the bathroom. The ceiling fan
sputters and chirps, and a spider, its web just begun,
frantically scoots toward a corner.

Through the open door, I can still see you sitting on the bed.
You lean over your book—back a tight curve—turn
another page, brush hair from your eyes
and begin to highlight the important passages.

Total Eclipse of the Moon

Our house is dark and cold.
I sit in my car in the driveway.
I've opened the sunroof,
lowered the seat back,
hold binoculars to my eyes,
watch darkness slowly glide
across the moon's face.
There's no hurry.
A meteor flashes, bright and gone.

I listen to the radio: *L.A. Woman*
by the Doors, *Vincent* by Don McLean.
The sky is sharp and cloudless.
There is no breeze, but November
penetrates the layers of shirts
and sweaters I wear, my fingers numb.

The car shifts as Alice, our butterscotch cat,
jumps on the hood, walks up the windshield,
pokes her head over the edge of the sunroof.
What are you doing? she asks. Why are you here?
Her head fills the sky as she waits, disappears
as she moves away, leaps off the car.

The moon is dark now, a shadow
rimmed in red, remnants of reflected light,
penumbral illusion of an illusion.
Things align and unalign: the earth
sun, moon—you & me.

Hide and Seek

The plant
beneath the lithograph
on the south wall
is still dying
and in the park
children play games, run
in circles, fall down
on purpose. Lately,
I fear my clocks
have become treacherous:
their tiny gears, turning
with infinitesimal glee,
have stolen my days
and the sun on my face
casts shadows
that will not go away.
"I no longer love you,"
she says, then frowns
as if testing the words.

Dust

27. The doctor says
probably an allergy.
Pollen. Or the smog.
He gives me pills—I
throw them away, of course.
28. The house grows worse;
every surface now gray-tinged.
29. I sit for hours
and sometimes I think
I must go somewhere,
for I blink and the clock
has changed—hours disappearing
like colored bubbles: pop,
pop, gone. 30. After eight years
she said she felt nothing
and left. 31. That's a record.
So many sneezes. You know
they've found that household dust
is 80% dead human skin cells?

Butterfly

I cut my thumb with a pair of blue scissors.
It was an accident. I was angry with a bank,
cutting up its MasterCard,
when the tip of the scissors
caught my thumb. I saw a butterfly.

For an instant that's what I thought
I really saw, a butterfly
sitting on the end of my thumb,
pale wings tipped with red
where the blades had lifted
two flaps of skin angled like wings
poised for flight.

In the bathroom, as I ran water
over the cuts, I thought of Norman Rush
in Africa, cresting a hill at sunset,
to stop, stunned by what he saw:
                              huge pulsating
globes of fire resting on the plain—
his mind locked and blank, grasping
for an explanation until he recognized
balls of elephant dung covered with butterflies,
thousands of wings fluttering in the sun's red light.
No references, he said—he'd had no references
to translate what he'd first seen, so far removed
from any prior experience.

And at three in the morning in my quiet apartment,
my thumb throbs as I hold a framed photograph,
seeing only unconnected dots in black & white,
wonder why after eight years you're gone, blood
rushing in my ears, like wings.

After My Divorce Was Followed
by the November Elections of 1994

It's all too much.
I want to be a turtle,
pull my arms and legs inside
some sweet and homey shell
where it's safe and dark
and I don't have to know
what the world is doing.
Knowing my luck, though,
I'll have stopped
in the middle of a road
and coming toward me,
just around the corner
over that rise is a cowboy
in a '62 Ford pickup,
a Budweiser between his legs,
thumping his calloused palm
against the steering wheel
as he listens to some
twangy country song about
lost love and hound dogs.
And at the last moment
he'll see me in his headlights,
swerve just enough
to squash me flat, splatter
my precious fluids across
this hot and sticky pavement.
I'd best keep moving.

Answering Machine

She leaves messages
on my answering machine,
asks for my help,
tells me things
I'd rather not know:

    her microwave clock
    is stuck on 12:00,
    the computer's screwing up,
    there's a book she can't find,
    at 38 her cousin Crystal
    has died of cancer.

You can't do this! I want to tell her.
We're divorced. It's not fair. Instead,
I call her back, explain the procedure
to reset the clock, tell her
I'll look for the book,
how bad I feel about Crystal.

And after I walk her through Norton
Utilities, defragment the hard disk,
and we're saying goodbye,
she asks how I'm doing, and
I tell her okay, I'm doing okay.

Gravity Is More Than the Power of Attraction

At 500 watts the halogen lamp fills the room with light,
bright as the sunshine I haven't seen in three days.
How did I land here at 4 a.m. in this heavy brown chair,
immobilized?

The moon is full today, the TV says, roils the waters
on the skin of our planet. I sit tilted back, my legs up.
I cannot see the moon, but sense the earth,
six-and-a-half sextillion tons that bind me to this chair.
I feel boneless.

I mute the TV, watch instead the books on my wall,
spines gleaming with gold filigree, soft leathers of fawn
and gray, russet and blue, in orderly rows, impervious
to gravity. I believe in words.

"That a marriage ends," says John Updike, "is less than
ideal; but all things end under heaven, and if temporality
is held to be invalidating, then nothing real succeeds."
Yes, I think, of course. I have to get on with my life.

Instead, I watch the ceiling, pebbled and white,
like some inverted south sea island beach. *So we won't
grow old together.* A fly walks the ceiling sands, upside
down and unconcerned. It drops and circles the room,
then climbs toward the lamp and its shriveling glare.
Don't land, I think, don't land—and I feel this sudden
overwhelming sense of compassion, await the odor
of burning.

Chasing Orange

Tonight a breeze slipped
through my bathroom window,
the scent of orange blossoms
like an offering—and I wanted
to shout *this is the wrong
altar, the wrong temple,
that god is dead.* Instead,
I allowed the old beast
memory to roam a while,
then dusted bookshelves
for three hours, pulled
every book out of its
cranny, ran fingers
over dust jackets, rubbed
shelves till they gleamed,
used an entire can of Pledge,
finally chased the scent
of oranges away.

Blue Earth

It'll pass, friends say, things
will get better with time.
Yes, I nod, and smile as I
glance outside at the green
sky and blue earth, admire
the shaggy roots of trees
whose thousands of fine
radicels wave and squirm
as they suck moisture
from the air. I inhale
chunks of terraqueous ooze
that soothe the capillaries
of my lungs, watch fat worms
wriggle through terra-cotta
clouds. Yes, I think,
I'm adapting—already
things are looking better.

Coit Tower

It's a photograph from our honeymoon, San Francisco,
a shot of our blue Honda Prelude, my wife's head
sticking up through the sunroof, a dazed smile.

Bright sunlight glares off the windshield, hides her body,
arms and hands, and it's just her face, short blonde hair
teased by the wind, that shows.

I should put the photo away, my therapist says.

At Coit Tower we sat in line almost an hour. I remember
the green smell of high banks along the street, small white
flowers, our laughter when we reached the tower, found it
closed.

Wreckage
October 1998

The woman sat in the middle of the street, hands
near her face, fingers wide and fluttering, as if playing
some strange musical instrument, blood flowing
in jagged lines down her forehead, fingertips turning red
where they tapped an unconscious rhythm
to accompany her moans: *my eyes, my eyes . . .*

My brother and I sat on our bicycles, watched
as rescue workers pulled bodies from the wreckage,
a fat policeman waving his arms—*get back! get back!
stay back!*—broken glass scattered like diamonds,
piles of treasure from a pirate's cave flickering
in the rhythmic fire of the patrol car's lights.

I was twelve. It was the summer of '62. It was the first time
I saw someone die. My brother and I had been watching TV
in our living room. It was almost 10:30 on a Saturday night,
almost time for bed, when we heard the crash a half-mile
away. My parents weren't home—out with friends—and
Clark and I grabbed our bikes, pedaled furiously
down Bethany Home Road and found the accident.

Two cars, a station wagon and a fire-engine-red Corvette
had crashed. At first, in my imagination, I think I thought
the driver of the Corvette was a spy, a good one,
and evil agents who were chasing him had shot out
his tires, laughing gleefully as they sped away
in their black limousine. The passengers in the station
wagon were innocent victims. That's how I thought of it
at first. But then I saw the bodies and the woman
with the blonde hair and her blood. And I realized
that this was no TV show, this was real. And I was scared.

And eight years later in Vietnam I was still scared. By then
I'd seen more death. But no spies. Although I understood
that they, too, were there—the CIA spooks—and I imagined
them, dressed in black, flitting from hamlet to hamlet.

Some nights I was sure I could hear them, whispering.
And some nights I think I came close to understanding
what they were saying—then a firefight or incoming
or merely sleep would pull me away and understanding
would be lost. And I was never sure whether that
was a good thing or a bad thing. I came home.
And bought a car and found a job and tried to put Vietnam
behind me. But some nights, when the whispering became
too strong, I would drive dark streets looking for a black
limousine.

I never found it. And eventually I stopped looking.
Which was good. And eventually I found a wife, a woman
who loved me despite my flaws, and that was even better.
And the whispers became a good thing. I loved her smile.
And her forehead; she had a beautiful forehead. She would
laugh when I told her that—that she had a gorgeous forehead.
She would say, you're a crazy man, and the skin
at the corners of her eyes would crinkle up from her smile
and I could see the love pouring off her in waves
of warm light. And I would agree that, yes, I was crazy—
about her. Then she would tell me I had a beautiful knee.
The left one. The right one, she'd say, was okay but not
beautiful, not even in the same league as my left knee.
We were incredibly silly.

We were together eight years. I know what you're thinking—
that she was killed in a car wreck. If this were a poorly written
television drama, that's what would happen next. But this isn't
TV. I don't know what happened. Something changed.
And she went away. And was no longer my wife. And I started
dreaming of Vietnam again. And every night I just wanted
to go to sleep and not wake up in the morning. But I did.
And nothing had changed. I know she's not coming back.

And my life goes on. And I think about that car wreck
sometimes. Those innocent people in the station wagon.
Were they coming home from a party? Or going to one?
Was the driver laughing at something silly a passenger
in the back seat had said? Or perhaps just smiling to himself
as his girlfriend, her long blonde hair smelling faintly

of strawberries, leaned against his shoulder? Were they
just unlucky? Hit by a drunk in a speeding Corvette?
Or was he the unlucky one? A station wagon
full of teenagers with fake IDs out in daddy's car
swerving drunkenly into the oncoming lane?
I don't know.

But I know I won't forget that young woman, blinded
by flying glass, who rocked in the street, her thick hair
falling across her face as she softly cried, *my eyes,
my eyes.* I sat there on my bicycle, wanting to help
but not knowing what to do, as firemen and paramedics—
these adults—ran from place to place, ignoring her cries.
And my arms began to shake, and I dropped my bike
and sat on the grass trembling, as I've sat on my bed
so many nights these last four years, blinded
by the unrelenting knowledge that Rebecca
is gone—that the war is never over.

Second Skin

Our water heater died last night, this morning a cold shower,
gritting my teeth, making it quick—face, armpits, crotch—in
and out. First cold shower since Vietnam.

In the officers' showers, water always ran hot. Wearing
flip-flops, fatigue pants and a T-shirt, anyone might be
a lieutenant. That day, I'd sneaked into officers' country,
the shower an eight-foot square of concrete enclosed
by waist-high plywood, wire screens, a tin roof—the
licorice-black roaches two inches long and sullen.

I'd just gotten soaped up good, water hot and better
than sex, when the first mortar shell blew out the kitchen
of the officer's mess, killing two cooks and a cat. The cat
was probably an accident, a stand-in for the officers
who would have been there had it been mealtime.

The siren, unnecessary as usual, screamed as soldiers
grabbed steel pots and rifles, jammed arms into flak jackets,
scurried toward bunkers. And somewhere on the base
some jerk following standard operating procedure
shut off the main water supply.

I stood in the shower, naked, covered with soap,
water from the showerhead slowing to a dribble.
Another mortar shell took out a latrine 40 yards away,
shrapnel pinging the roof, a small hole opening in the wall
next to me. Men ran in circles, yelling—small-arms fire
from the perimeter, an M-60 machine gun opening up.
Fuck it, I thought, sitting down. *I'm not moving
till they turn the water back on.*

The soap made interesting patterns as it dried,
tightening like a second skin or the exoskeleton
of a freshly hatched insect. My skin began to itch.
The roaches, which had disappeared when I turned
the shower on, returned in twos and threes, antennae
twitching, wondering if I were lunch.

Six months later, flying home, my time as a soldier
almost over, I stared at the ocean from the window

of our 727, waves like wrinkled skin, water sparking
as sunlight danced the crests, clouds laying down
bands of shadow, appearing and disappearing.

Men are more watery than women. That's what scientists
claim—10 to 15 percent—some parts more liquid
than others: bones 22 percent water, muscle 75 percent
and blood, the wateriest of all. I read that once.

The article never mentioned water content of the brain
or the tides that move between its hemispheres, waves
that surge through our lives, at times icy storms,
at times soothing as sunlight or the words of a lover . . .

. . . years later my wife trying to teach me French
while we showered, our bodies close and slick,
the water rinsing us clean as she whispered in my ear
je t'adore—my repeated attempts to replicate her words
growing more inept until I settled on *shut the door, shut
the door,* and we stood there, laughing at our silliness,
water streaming down our faces, our warm bodies,
ourselves without fear.

December 13, 2001

At odd moments all day today, the thought
    that it was your birthday would pop
    into my mind, and I would wonder
    if you're happy. 51. For five days
    we'll be the same age.

Have you also been receiving letters
    encouraging you to join AARP?
    It's scary. Remember the time
    we searched the Internet for events
    that took place on your birthday?

In 1577, Sir Francis Drake left
    on his round-the-world trip. But he
    completely missed New Zealand,
    discovered in the mid-1600s
    on December 13 by some Dutch navigator.

And in 1978, the Susan B. Anthony dollar
    began production on your birthday,
    how pleased you were that it was
    the first U.S. coin
    to honor a woman.

But December 13, 1972, is the one
    that sticks—the day U.S. astronauts
    left the moon for the last time.
    I don't think anyone expected
    it would be the last time.

There were so many expectations, such high hopes
    then. We were both 22 that day. I wish
    I had known you then. We met so late,
    so much history behind us, so much
    to weigh us down.

Each December you beginning a new age,
    me poised to leave that one

behind—exploring the decades we'd
spent apart, mapping the few years
we shared.

It was beautiful here today—cool but sunny,
so clear you could see the Cuyamacas
from La Jolla, the mountains dark yet inviting,
air crisp with a salt breeze off the ocean—
a day full of promise.

***A note on the poem* 12 Pennies**

For those readers who care about such things, here is my solution to the 12 pennies brainteaser:

Problem: You have 12 pennies. One is bad, either too heavy or too light. You have a balance scale, but can use it only three times. Determine which penny is bad and whether it is too heavy or too light.

Solution: Divide the coins into three groups of four coins each: A_{1-4}, B_{1-4}, C_{1-4}.

Weigh (1)	A_{1-4}	B_{1-4}	If balanced, then the bad coin is in group C.
Weigh (2a)	A_{1-3}	C_{1-3}	If balanced, then C_4 is the bad coin.
Weigh (3a)	A_1	C_4	This will determine if C_4 is heavy or light.

If (2a) is unbalanced, then C_1, C_2 or C_3 is bad, and I know the bad coin is either heavy or light depending on which way the scale moves.

Weigh (3b)	C_1	C_2	If balanced, then C_3 is bad and I know whether it is heavy or light because of (2a); if unbalanced, then either C_1 or C_2 is the bad coin and I know which one, also because of (2a).

If weigh (1) — A_{1-4} | B_{1-4} — is unbalanced, then the bad coin is in group A or B. For clarity, rename the heavy-side coins H_{1-4} and the light-side coins L_{1-4}. Group C remains C.

Weigh (2b)	H_1, L_1, C_1	H_2, L_2, L_3	There are three possible outcomes:

1st Outcome: If weigh (2b) is balanced, then L_4 is light or H_3 or H_4 is heavy.

Weight (3c)	L_4, H_4	C_1, C_2	If balanced, then H_3 is the bad coin and is heavy. If unbalanced (down on left), then H_4 is the bad coin and is heavy. If

unbalanced (up on left), then
L_4 is the bad coin and is light.

2nd Outcome: If weigh (2b) is unbalanced (down on the left), then
H_1 is heavy or L_2 or L_3 is light.

Weigh (3d) L_2, H_1 | C_1, C_2 If balanced, then L_3 is the bad
coin and is light. If unbalanced
(down on left), then H_1 is the bad
coin and is heavy. If unbalanced
(up on left), then L_2 is the bad
coin and is light.

3rd Outcome: If weigh (2b) is unbalanced (up on the left), then L_1 is
light or H_2 is heavy.

Weigh (3e) L_1 | C_1 If balanced, then H_2 is the bad
coin and is heavy. If unbalanced,
then L_1 is the bad coin and is light.

Terry Hertzler

Versions of some of the pieces
in this book appeared in:

Stand Up Poetry: The Anthology
In the Palm of Your Hand: The Poet's Portable Workshop
San Diego Reader
California Quarterly
Los Angeles Times
San Diego Union-Tribune
City Works
San Diego Writers' Monthly
The No-Street Poets' Voice
The Poetry Conspiracy
The Veteran
Deros
Incoming!
Visions Magazine
The Zoo Where You're Fed to God
Total Eclipse of the Moon
Life on the Border
The Way of the Snake
The Magee Park Poets Anthology
San Diego Home/Garden Lifestyles
We Accept Donations

Terry Hertzler has worked as a writer and editor for more than 20 years, writing for magazines and newspapers, as well as producing sales, marketing, PR and technical documents for a variety of commercial and non-profit organizations. He has taught writing—including composition, poetry and technical writing—at the university level as well as for The Writing Center and the Southern California Writers' Conference. His poetry and short stories have appeared in a variety of publications, including *Stand Up Poetry: An Expanded Anthology* (University of Iowa Press), *In the Palm of Your Hand: The Poet's Portable Workshop* (Tilbury House, Publishers), *California Quarterly*, the *Los Angeles Times* and *The Veteran*, as well as being produced on stage and for radio and television. His publications include *The Way of the Snake*, a book of poetry on the war in Vietnam, and several other books of poetry and fiction. He owns Caernarvon Press, which has published the work of more than a dozen authors since 1985, including LoVerne Brown, Brandon Cesmat, Forrest Curo, Steve Kowit, Ken Kuhlken, Robert Richards, Alan Russell, Peggy Shumaker, Karen Stromberg and Al Zolynas, and is a founder of the San Diego Writers' Cooperative (www.sandiegowriters.org). He has also owned two bookstores and sells rare and collectible books on the Internet. Hertzler served with the 101st Airborne Division in Vietnam, 1969-70. He is an addicted reader, an audiophile and owns two motorcycles.

ISBN 0-9716383-2-2

Caernarvon Press
San Diego